A Note to Parents

DK READERS is a compelling programme for beginning readers, designed in conjunction with leading lit— experts, including Maureen Fern— Maureen has spent many years te classroom and as a specialist in sc

Beautiful illustrations and superb f ......ographs combine with engaging, easy-to-read stories to offer a fresh approach to each subject in the series. Each DK READER is guaranteed to capture a child's interest while developing his or her reading skills, general knowledge and love of reading.

The five levels of DK READERS are aimed at different reading abilities, enabling you to choose the books that are exactly right for your child:

Pre-level 1: Learning to read
Level 1: Beginning to read
Level 2: Beginning to read alone
Level 3: Reading alone
Level 4: Proficient readers

The "normal" age at which a child begins to read can be anywhere from three to eight years old. Adult participation through the lower levels is very helpful for providing encouragement, discussing storylines and sounding out unfamiliar words.

No matter which level you select, you can be sure that you are helping your child learn to read, then read to learn!

For Dorling Kindersley
Senior Editor Laura Gilbert
Senior Designers Lisa Sodeau,
David McDonald
Slipcase Designer Stefan Georgiou
Pre-Production Producer Kavita Varma
Senior Producer Alex Bell
Managing Editor Sadie Smith
Managing Art Editor Ron Stobbart
Creative Manager Sarah Harland
Art Director Lisa Lanzarini
Publisher Julie Ferris
Publishing Director Simon Beecroft

Reading Consultant Maureen Fernandes

For Lucasfilm
Executive Editor J. W. Rinzler
Art Director Troy Alders
Keeper of the Holocron Leland Chee
Director of Publishing Carol Roeder

This edition published in 2016
First published in Great Britain in 2012
by Dorling Kindersley Limited,
80 Strand, London, WC2R 0RL

Slipcase UI: 001-305124-Oct/16

Page design copyright © 2016 Dorling Kindersley Limited.
A Penguin Random House Company

© and TM 2016 LUCASFILM LTD.

A CIP catalogue record for this book
is available from the British Library

ISBN: 978-1-4093-7481-7

Printed in China.

www.starwars.com
www.dk.com

A WORLD OF IDEAS:
SEE ALL THERE IS TO KNOW

Contents

DK READERS

STAR WARS

WHO SAVED THE GALAXY?

Written by Catherine Saunders

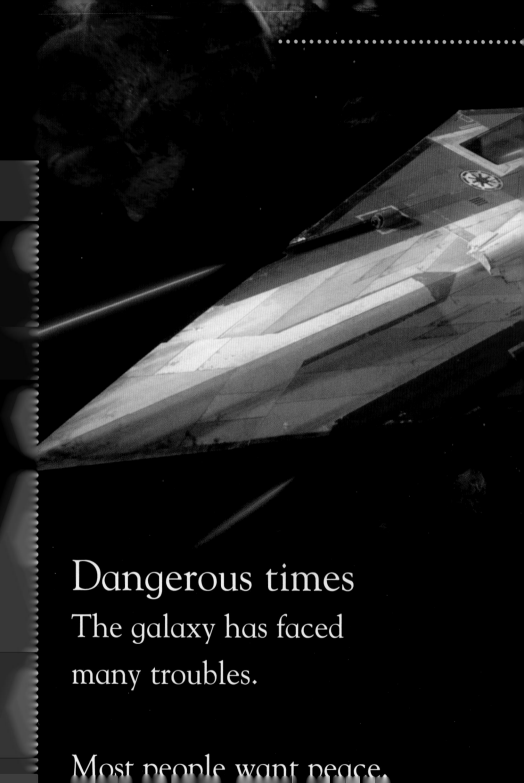

Dangerous times

The galaxy has faced
many troubles.

Most people want peace.

But some people want
to start wars.

Who can keep the galaxy safe?
It is a dangerous job. . .

The Jedi

The Jedi believe in peace and justice.

The Jedi Council

However, sometimes even the Jedi must fight to keep the galaxy safe.

During the Battle of Geonosis, many brave Jedi fought to defeat the Separatists and their droid army.

Obi-Wan Kenobi

Obi-Wan Kenobi

Jedi Knight Obi-Wan Kenobi was known as "the Negotiator".

He was also a brave fighter.

He defeated a Sith called Darth Maul in a duel.

Obi-Wan fought against the
Dark Sith Lord called
Darth Vader in a battle.

Obi-Wan sacrificed his own
life so that the galaxy
could be saved.

Master Yoda

This brave Jedi saved the galaxy many times.

He had great
Force powers
and was
skilled with
a lightsaber.

He duelled the Sith Lords
Dooku and Palpatine.

Yoda also trained many Jedi,
including Luke Skywalker.

Dooku —

The Clone Army

During the Clone Wars, the Clone Army fought side by side with the Jedi.

Each trooper was brave, obedient and identical.

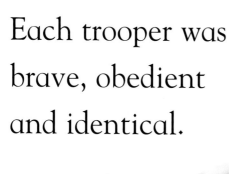

protective armour

However, the troopers had a secret master.

At his command they changed from saving the galaxy to helping to destroy it.

The Rebels

The Rebel Alliance are
a very brave group of people.

They risked their lives to free
the galaxy from the evil
Emperor Palpatine.

The rebels destroyed both
the Emperor's superweapons
called the Death Stars.

They showed the people of the
galaxy that they did not need
to live in fear any more.

R2-D2

Princess Leia

Leia is a princess
and a senator from the
planet Alderaan.

She is also a rebel leader.

Princess Leia risked her life
many times to save the galaxy.

She helped the rebels
to destroy both Death Stars.

Han Solo

Some people don't mean
to save the galaxy.

Han Solo was a smuggler,
not a hero.

He helped the Rebel Alliance
on one mission.

Soon after, he was helping them to defeat Emperor Palpatine.

Chewbacca

Han Solo

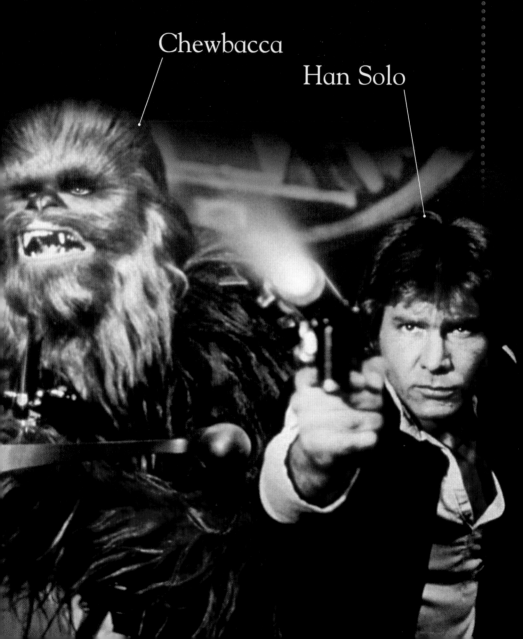

Anakin Skywalker

Anakin Skywalker was one of the greatest Jedi ever known.

He first saved the galaxy when he was a young boy.

R2-D2

Later, Anakin became
a Jedi Knight and went
on many missions.

However, Anakin
was not able to
resist the power
of the dark side.

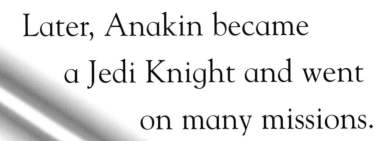

belt

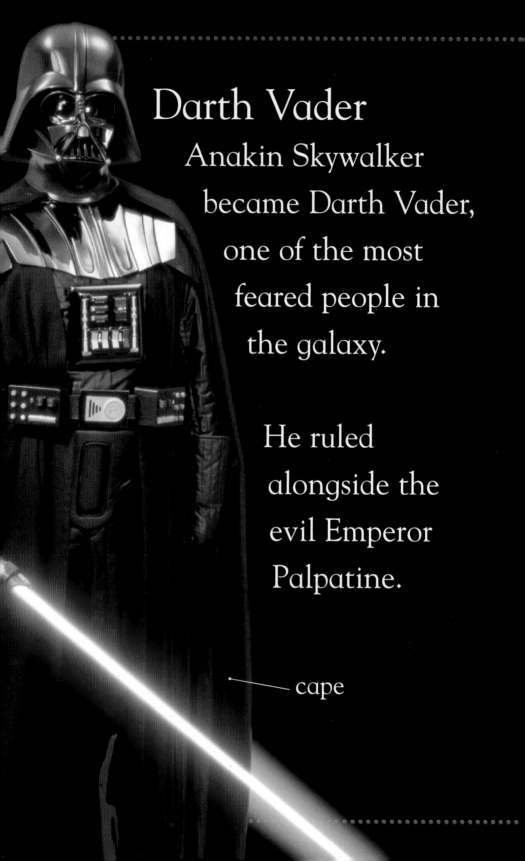

Darth Vader

Anakin Skywalker
became Darth Vader,
one of the most
feared people in
the galaxy.

He ruled
alongside the
evil Emperor
Palpatine.

— cape

When the Emperor tried to attack Darth Vader's son, Luke, Vader destroyed Palpatine.

Darth Vader saved Luke.

He also freed the galaxy from the Emperor.

Luke Skywalker

Luke Skywalker is a Jedi.
He became part of the Rebel
Alliance.

He fired the shot that destroyed
the first Death Star.

Luke had the strength to resist the power of the dark side.

His courage helped to unite the galaxy. He even fought Darth Vader.

The Ewoks

These small, furry creatures don't look like they could save the galaxy!

However, they helped the rebels to defeat Emperor Palpatine.

The Ewoks attacked Imperial
stormtroopers. This meant
the rebels could attack
the Death Star.

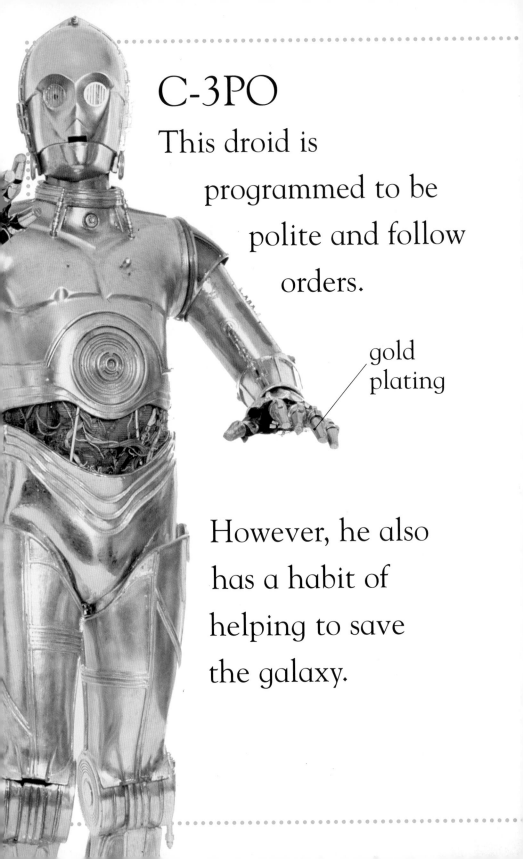

C-3PO

This droid is programmed to be polite and follow orders.

gold plating

However, he also has a habit of helping to save the galaxy.

It was C-3PO who convinced
the Ewoks to help the Jedi.

He happened to look just like
an Ewok god!

R2-D2

R2-D2 is a very brave and
clever droid.

He can co-pilot spaceships,
and fix them.

R2-D2 helped Anakin Skywalker, Princess Leia and Luke Skywalker to save the galaxy.

Who do you think truly saved the galaxy?

Glossary

Dark side
The part of the Force associated with fear and hatred.

Droid army
A group of droids who fight. Droids are a type of robot.

Dueled
Fought, or battled.

Force powers
The energy created by all living things.

Jedi
People who can sense the energy created by all living things. This energy is called the Force.

Jedi Council
A group of Jedi and Jedi Masters who oversee all the other Jedi.

Lightsaber
A weapon that looks like a sword and has a blade made of pure energy.

Negotiator
Someone who discusses something in order to reach an agreement.

Obedient
Following orders. Willing to obey.

Sacrificed
Given up something for the sake of something else that's considered to be more worthy.

Separatists
A group of people who want to separate themselves from the Galactic Republic.

Sith
Enemies of the Jedi who use the dark side of the Force.

Smuggler
Someone who takes goods to a country or planet illegally.